THE CONDUIT

Title Page Art by: Jesús Saiz

DOWN

7 Down: Vacationed in MIDNIGHT MASS
21 Down: Joined THE RESISTANCE
33 Down: Looking forward to the TWILIGHT EXPERIMENT

ACROSS

25 Across: Busted by the ABSOLUTE AUTHORITY
48 Across: Dances the TWO-STEP
56 Across: Drinks from a HIP FLASK
67 Across: He's got us COVERED

BY RIGHTS, THIS BOOK SHOULD NOT EXIST.

WHICH IS NOT TO SAY THERE'S ANYTHING WRONG WITH IT; ON THE CONTRARY, 21 DOWN IS A GREAT READ. AN INTELLIGENT STORY VERY WELL WRITTEN AND DRAWN, WITH INTERESTING CHARACTERS WHO DON'T REVEAL THEMSELVES ALL IN ONE BREATHLESS, ONE-PAGE RUSH. A BOOK THAT KEEPS YOU GUESSING. BUT THAT'S NOT REALLY ENOUGH THESE DAYS, IS IT?

COMICS—MONTHLY COMICS, AT ANY RATE—ARE NOT DOING TERRIBLY WELL AT THE MOMENT. SALES HAVE BEEN DECLINING STEADILY SINCE THE GIGANTIC ACT OF SELF-BUGGERY THAT WAS SPECULATOR-DRIVEN PUBLISHING FINALLY CAME TO AN END. PLENTY OF NEW COMICS ARE STILL BEING RELEASED, GRANTED, BUT PRECIOUS FEW OF THEM MANAGE TO SURVIVE LONGER THAN A YEAR—AND BY NEW I MEAN **NEW**, NOT SOME LONG-ESTABLISHED SUPERHERO UNDERGOING YET ANOTHER REVIVAL WITH YET ANOTHER "NEW TWIST." IT'S A HOSTILE MARKET RIGHT NOW, AND PLENTY OF GOOD STUFF GETS FLUSHED DOWN THE CRAPPER ALONG WITH THE BAD.

SO IT CAME AS QUITE A SURPRISE TO READ A BOOK THAT MAKES NO CONCESSIONS TO THE CURRENT CLIMATE WHATSOEVER.

NOW, I PERSONALLY BELIEVE THAT YOU NEED TO HIT THE READER RIGHT BETWEEN THE EYES WHEN LAUNCHING NEW MATERIAL; YOU GRAB THEIR ATTENTION FIRST AND LET THE QUIET, SUBTLE STUFF CREEP IN AROUND THE EDGES LATER. NOT THESE GUYS, THOUGH—ALL THEY CONCERN THEMSELVES WITH IS TELLING A DAMN FINE STORY. AND—WHAT I THINK I LIKE MOST ABOUT THIS PUPPY— THEY TAKE THEIR OWN SWEET TIME DOING IT, TOO.

IT WON'T BE UNTIL TOWARDS THE END OF THIS TRADE PAPERBACK COLLECTION THAT YOU'LL FULLY UNDERSTAND THE MELANCHOLY PRESTON KILLS AND THE PRICKLY RELATIONSHIP HE HAS WITH HIS BROTHER; NOT UNTIL THE VERY LAST PAGE WILL YOU EVEN BEGIN TO GET A HANDLE ON MICKEY RINALDI. THE NICE THING IS THAT YOU'RE GOING TO ENJOY GETTING THERE, WATCHING MICKEY (THE BOOK'S BEST CHARACTER) STRING PRESTON ALONG EVEN THOUGH HE KNOWS HE'S BEING PLAYED. 21 DOWN, YOU SEE, SPORTS SUCH AN INTRIGUING SUPPORTING CAST AND SUCH NICELY WRITTEN DIALOGUE THAT ITS STEADY PACE BECOMES AN ASSET RATHER THAN A SETBACK. YOU WON'T HAVE THE MEASURE OF THIS STORY BY THE END OF ITS FIRST OR SECOND CHAPTER—SOMETHING FOR WHICH YOU'LL BE THOROUGHLY GRATEFUL.

SO WHAT WERE THEY THINKING, THE WRITERS OF 21 DOWN, TRYING TO MAKE A GO OF A BOOK LIKE THIS ONE WHILE OTHER COMICS WERE FALLING LIKE NINEPINS? NOT LONG AFTER THE RELEASE OF THE FIRST ISSUE I ASKED JIMMY PALMIOTTI THAT VERY QUESTION; HE WAS IN THE BASEMENT OF HIS BROOKLYN APARTMENT BUILDING AT THE TIME, WHERE I FOUND HIM RESTOCKING HIS FREEZER WITH MEAT.

"GREAT BOOK, JIMMY, BUT DO YOU REALLY EXPECT IT TO SURVIVE? NO SUPERHERO STUFF, NOT MUCH ACTION, LOTS OF TALKIE SCENES..."

"YEAH, YEAH."

"I MEAN YOU COULD MEET CHARACTERS LIKE THESE WALKING DOWN THE STREET—OR MOST OF THEM, ANYWAY..."

"YEAH, YEAH."

"YOU NEED TO HAVE SOMETHING FREAKY HAPPEN. SOMETHING THAT'LL BLOW THE READERS OUT OF THEIR SOCKS."

"YEAH, YEAH."

"THAT'S, UH...THAT'S MICKEY'S DRESS YOU'RE WEARING, ISN'T IT? FROM ISSUE FOUR?"

(CLENCHING HIS BLOOD-SLICK FISTS) "NO, IT'S HARMONY'S FROM #2. WHAT ARE YOU, BLIND?"

"I HAVE TO GO NOW, MATE."

JUSTIN GRAY WAS EVEN LESS HELP THAN JIMMY. I CALLED THE SOMETIME CHEF/FOSSIL HUNTER/BULL CASTRATOR * AT HIS HOME IN WESTCHESTER, HOPING VAINLY FOR ANSWERS...

"SO, JUSTIN, I WAS WONDERING—"

"IT WAS ALL MY IDEA."

"WHAT?"

"EVERYTHING, THE WHOLE STORY, I CAME UP WITH ALL OF IT. PALMIOTTI'S A LOSER; I'M JUST TRADING ON HIS NAME UNTIL MY GENIUS IS RECOGNIZED."

"BUT—"

"JUST PUT 'IT WAS ALL JUSTIN'S IDEA.' DO IT. DO IT OR I'LL OPEN FIRE INTO THE CROWD."

"UH..."

THUS ENDETH THE SEARCH FOR ENLIGHTENMENT...

PERHAPS, THOUGH, JIMMY AND JUSTIN HAD SIMPLY PEGGED ME AS A DIMWIT AND WERE WAITING FOR ME TO CATCH ON TO THE GLARINGLY OBVIOUS: THAT EVERYONE INVOLVED IN THE BOOK DID A BRILLIANT JOB; THAT EVEN WITH THINGS THE WAY THEY ARE NOWADAYS, THAT CAN STILL BE ENOUGH TO SWING THE DEAL; THAT 21 DOWN SURVIVES BECAUSE IT'S GREAT.

AND SURVIVE IT HAS, WITH THIS COLLECTION AND THE FORTHCOMING MATURE READERS-LABELLED RELAUNCH BEARING TESTAMENT TO ITS SUCCESS. LONG MAY IT CONTINUE, TOO; I'M KEEN TO KNOW WHERE THIS THING'S GOING, AS ARE A LOT OF OTHER PEOPLE. ANOTHER GREAT COMIC TO KEEP US ALL IN SUSPENSE—AND, I SUPPOSE, JIMMY IN DRESSES AND JUSTIN IN 30.06 AMMUNITION.

ONE LAST THOUGHT. IF, IN YEARS TO COME, YOU'RE READING THE UMPTEENTH REPRINTING OF THIS VOLUME IN SOME UTOPIAN AGE OF COMIC BOOK PUBLISHING—WITH COMICS ABOUT EVERYTHING, COMICS FOR EVERYONE, AND COSTUMED SUPERHEROES EITHER STUCK IN A TINY GHETTO-LIKE IMPRINT OR REINVENTED BEYOND ALL RECOGNITION—AND YOU'RE WONDERING ABOUT MY GLOOMY VIEW OF THE INDUSTRY, HERE'S WHAT HAPPENED: YES, THINGS WERE BAD. BUT, EVENTUALLY, THEY GOT BETTER. AND IT WAS MOSTLY THANKS TO BOOKS LIKE 21 DOWN.

- GARTH ENNIS
MAY 28TH, 2003 A.D

* ALL TRUE

ONE HOUR LATER.

ALL DONE.

NOT YET.

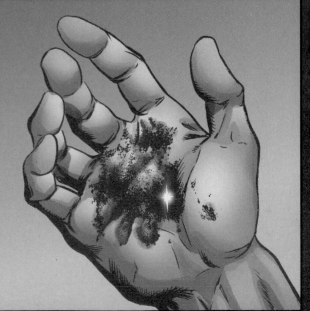

SIMPLE KIND OF LIFE

"I HATE THAT YOU ASK ME TO DO THIS."

"IS THAT YOUR IDEA OF A JOKE?"

"CAN YOU SEE THE NAME OF THE PLACE? ANYTHING FAMILIAR, A MATCHBOOK, LOGO? GIVE ME SOMETHING."

"NO NAME, UNDERGROUND, BLACK DOOR LIKE CLUB SIBERIA. EVERYTHING IS A BIT...OFF. SOMEONE IS MOVING TO HER ACROSS THE ROOM...SMELLS LIKE SWEAT, ROSEWATER... AND FORMALDEHYDE?"

"FOR WHAT IT'S WORTH, I'M SORRY. LEAST IT'S ONLY ONE BODY THIS TIME."

"THEY ARE IN THE ALLEY WHERE YOU FOUND HER...WENT OUT THE BACK DOOR OF THE CLUB. SHE KNOWS HIM...I THINK. CAN'T MAKE *HIM* OUT, HE'S BACKLIT, AND SHE IS HIGH. SHE'S GETTING OFF ON THIS GUY. STUPID GIRL..."

COME TO THIS FATAL HOUR, WHEN AT LAST FROM THE EYES OF DELUDED MAN THE SCALES MUST FALL AWAY, AND BE SHOWN THE CRUEL PICTURES OF HIS ERRORS AND HIS VICES --
-- MY GIRL, DO YOU NOT REPENT THE HOST OF SINS UNTO WHICH YOU WERE LED BY WEAKNESS AND HUMAN FRAILTY?

"ROBERT, HE'S A SECTION 8, MAN... I CAN'T WATCH THIS..."

"HE TOOK HER FROM THE CLUB TO THE ALLEY ON EMMONS... WHERE YOU FOUND HER. I'M STOPPING HERE. IT'S ALL I CAN GIVE YOU."

SECOND SKIN. THE BEST TATTOO SHOP IN CONEY ISLAND. I KNOW THIS 'CAUSE I WORK THERE.

AS USUAL FOR A FRIDAY NIGHT, THE PLACE IS FILLED WITH MIDNIGHT VULTURES: THE NEO-TRIBAL, THE RAVER GIRLS IN TUBE TOPS AND HIP-HUGGERS LOOKING TO GET THEIR BELLIES PIERCED, THE GOTH PUNKS, RUSSIAN MOB PUNKS, THE BIKERS, THE PSEUDO-ADVENTUROUS YUPPIE ON A DARE.

YOU GET THE PICTURE.

WHAT DID YOU SAY?

I JUST KNOW THIS IS DEACON'S WORK, HE'S BEEN IN SING SING FOR THE LAST EIGHT YEARS AND IT'S AMAZING WHAT HE DOES WITH A BALLPOINT, ESPECIALLY UNDER THOSE CONDITIONS...

I DID A LITTLE TIME ON A B&E, BUT I GOT OUT IN '97 AND I'VE BEEN A CHOIRBOY EVER SINCE. DEACON AND I WERE IN D-BLOCK TOGETHER. END OF STORY, UNDERSTAND?

DO WHAT YOU HAVE TO, JUST MAKE SURE THE SPIDER WEBS GO ALL AROUND THE FINGERS TO THE BACK OF THE HAND WHERE THE SPIDER IS AND BACK TO THE FINGER NAILS.

YOU GOT IT. GONNA DO THE TOPS OF THE FINGERS FIRST, MAKE SURE THERE ISN'T A LOT OF BLEEDING.

UH-HUH. JUST DO IT.

NOT HERE... NOT NOW.

YEAH. LISTEN, DEREK, I GOTTA CLEAN THE SURFACE OF THE SKIN IN ORDER FOR THE TATTOO TO STAY CLEAN-LINED.

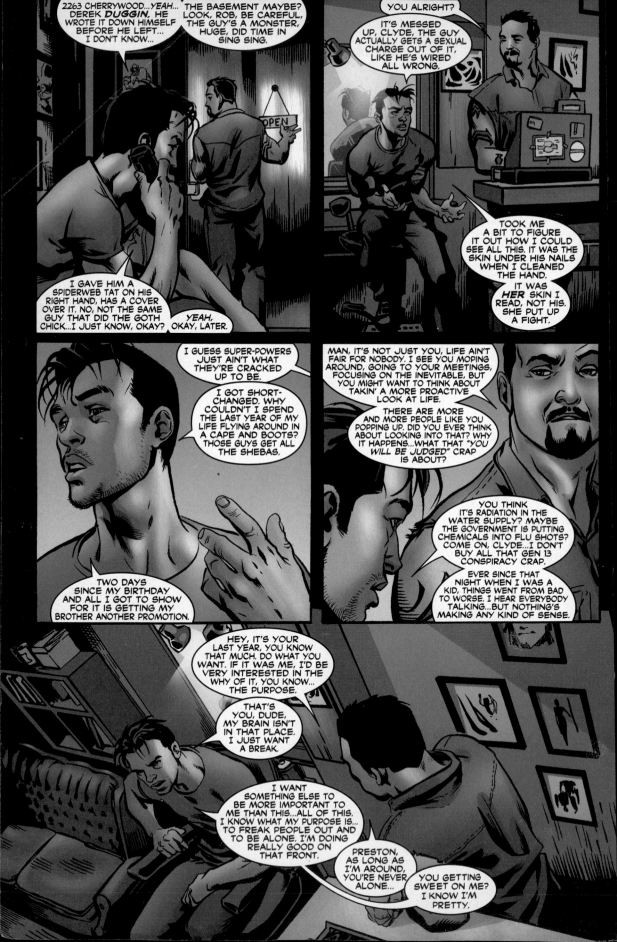

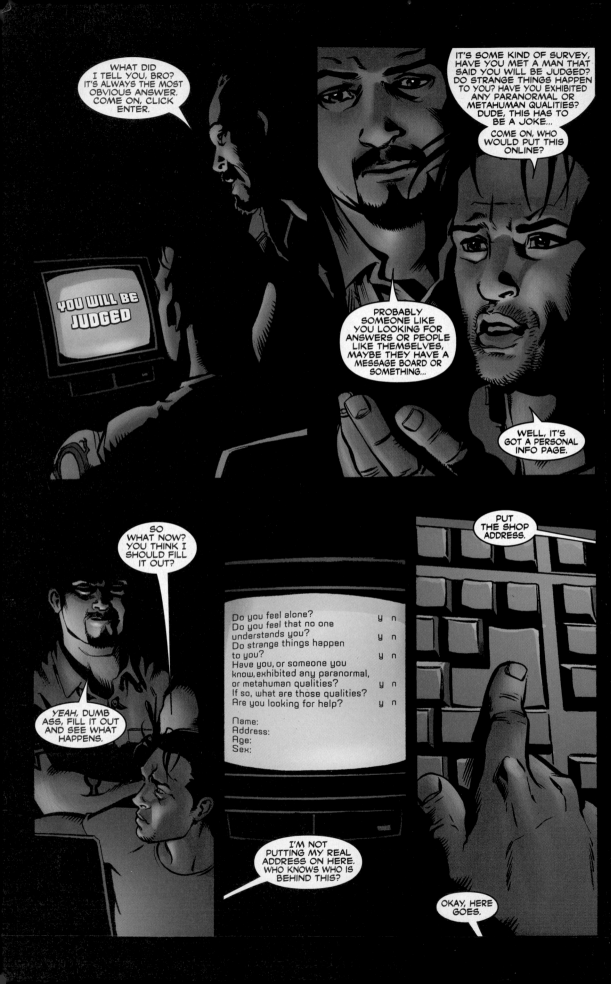

MICKEY

It was important when we first developed the character that Mickey physically conveyed an icy sexuality, a sense of determination and mystery. She had to be the exotic older woman, desirable but aloof and unattainable at the same time. She has all the classic sensual features—the high cheekbones, sensual eyes, full lips…well, you get the idea.

I LIKE TO WEAR SHEEP'S CLOTHING

YOUR BROTHER SEEMED PRETTY HAPPY WHEN I TURNED OVER THE COLLAR ON THAT PSYCHO BACK AT THE TATTOO PARLOR.

YEAH, WELL, HE LIKES WHEN PEOPLE HAND HIM THINGS. I'M JUST GLAD CLYDE'S OKAY.

WHAT ABOUT YOU, PRESTON?

WHAT ABOUT ME?

ARE YOU OKAY?

IT'S NOT EASY SEEING A MAN KILLED IN FRONT OF YOUR EYES AND HAVE A FRIEND IN THE EMERGENCY ROOM.

...I REALLY DON'T WANT TO TALK ABOUT THIS OR ME OR WHAT HAPPENED YESTERDAY OR LAST YEAR.

WHAT I WANT TO KNOW IS WHY YOU SHOWED UP, AND WHY YOU'RE OPERATING THAT WEBSITE.

WHAT ARE YOU LOOKING FOR?

SO, TELL ME, AGENT RINALDI, WHY IS THE FBI USING A WEBSITE TO LOCATE... FREAKS?

YOU'RE NOT A FREAK, PRESTON, AND PLEASE CALL ME MICKEY. I WANT US TO BE FRIENDS.

TO ANSWER YOUR QUESTION, OVER THE PAST FEW MONTHS THERE HAS BEEN A STEADY INCREASE IN GENIE ACTIVITY.

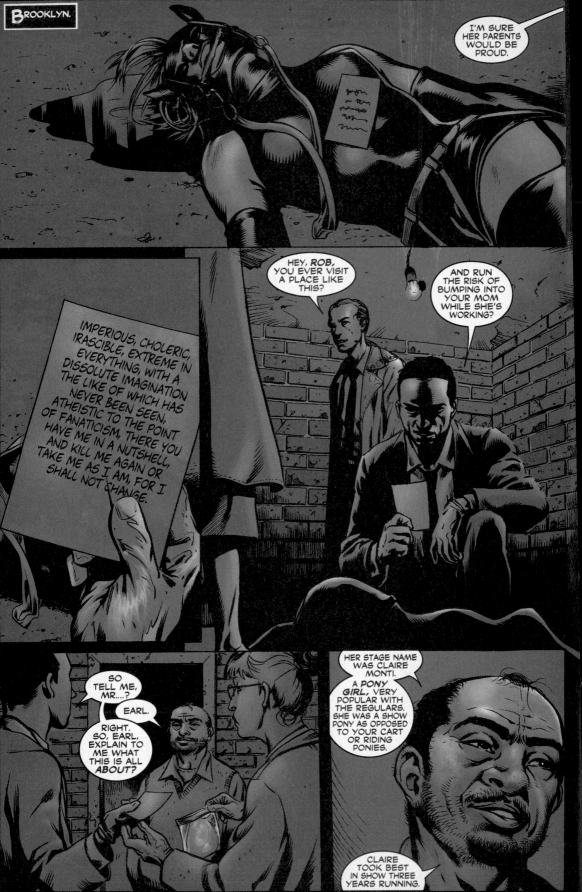

MAD DOG

Mad Dog is a morose bastard, drug dealer and ex-con who's read too many serial killer autobiographies and has brainwashed himself into thinking it's his calling. A violent loser on a downward spiral.

HARMONY

Harmony represents that **girl** in high school. You know—the one who could make the boys crazy with a look and girls jealous with a word; maybe she was the head cheerleader. Maybe she ruled the cliques and was surrounded by clones of herself. The spoiled little rich girl everyone secretly hated yet would stop at nothing to do a favor for.

I'm Not Sick, But I'm Not Well

LET ME TELL YOU ABOUT SPECIAL AGENT *MICKEY RINALDI.*

ALL I DID WAS PLUG MY NAME INTO A WEBSITE CALLED *YOUWILLBEJUDGED.COM.* THEN, LAST NIGHT, AS SOME DERANGED SERIAL KILLER WAS TRYING TO STRANGLE ME TO DEATH, SHE CAME ALONG AND DUMPED A BULLET IN HIS CRANIUM.

TURNS OUT IT WAS HER WEBSITE, PART OF SOME GOVERNMENT PET PROJECT TO INVESTIGATE *GENIES*-- GENETICALLY ENHANCED PEOPLE.

YEAH, I KNOW WHAT YOU'RE THINKING, NOT THE MOST *IMAGINATIVE* CODENAME, THAT'S THE GOVERNMENT FOR YOU.

SEEMS THAT MY CURSE OF BEING ABLE TO "EXPERIENCE" SOMEONE'S DEATH HAS MADE ME PART OF THE BIG PICTURE IN AGENT RINALDI'S INVESTIGATION.

WHEN YOU KNOW YOU GOT LESS THAN A YEAR TO LIVE, YOU CAN EITHER STAY HOME AND CRY OR GET OUT AND DO SOMETHING ABOUT IT.

ONE LOOK AT MICKEY AND EVEN YOU MIGHT START TO BELIEVE SHE COULD HELP. AT THIS POINT I HAVE NOTHING TO LOSE...

...BUT TIME.

TONIGHT, I'M STANDING ON THE PORCH OF A SEVEN-MILLION-DOLLAR HOME IN SCARSDALE LOOKING FOR ANSWERS ABOUT SOME CREEPY GUY THAT LIKES TO CURSE KIDS WITH SUPERPOWERS.

LIFE IS FULL OF SURPRISES.

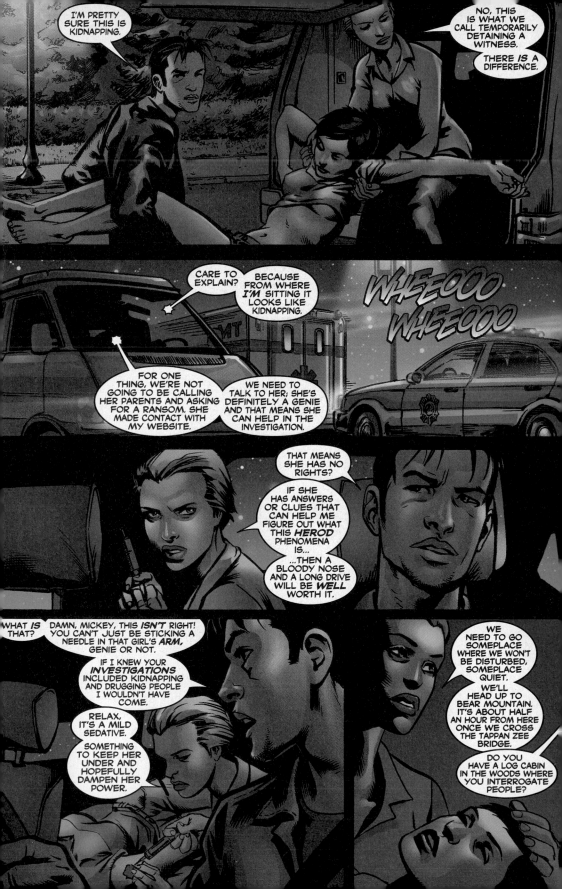

THIS IS *EXACTLY* THE SORT OF DEMENTED SITUATION THAT ANY RATIONAL, CLEAR-THINKING PERSON WOULD AVOID.

WITH EVERY STEP I TAKE DOWN THIS HILL, I FEEL LIKE I'M SINKING DEEPER INTO SOMETHING I WON'T BE ABLE TO ESCAPE FROM.

EVERY LITTLE BREEZE SEEMS TO WHISPER *"TURN AROUND."*

EVERY RUSTLE OF THE TREES SAYS, *"FORGET LITTLE MISS FOXY F.B.I. AGENT AND HER GENIE INITIATIVE. TAKE THIS POOR GIRL HOME AND THEN HITCHHIKE BACK TO BROOKLYN BEFORE SOMETHING REALLY BAD HAPPENS."*

FACT IS, THIS GIRL MIGHT HAVE ANSWERS.

BUT BY MICKEY SEDATING HER, SHE'S LOSING TIME, SHE'S DYING FASTER. THAT'S WORSE THAN KIDNAPPING...THAT'S MURDER.

HOW CAN I TRUST SOMEONE LIKE THAT?

WHAT'S TO STOP HER FROM DOING THE SAME THING TO ME? WHY IS SHE BOTHERING WITH *ME*, WHY NOT GRAB AN ACTUAL SUPERHERO?

I'M NOT A CAPE-WEARING SOCIALIST THAT BELIEVES HE CAN SOLVE ALL THE WORLD'S PROBLEMS WITH A RIGHT HOOK AND A SMILE.

TWO DAYS AGO I WAS PERFECTLY CONTENT WITH MY DECISIONS, AT PEACE WITH THE IDEA THAT I WAS GOING TO DIE AT 21.

NOW I'M NOT SO SURE. I WANT TO BLAME MICKEY, BUT I'D BE LYING TO MYSELF IF I SAID IT WAS ALL HER FAULT.

THE TRUTH IS...I DON'T REALLY WANT TO DIE.

WHEN DID I BECOME SUCH A WUSS?

"I HAD NO IDEA HOW *RIGHT* I WAS...

"SOMETHING, SOMEONE...WAS THERE, IN THE ROOM WITH ME.

"IT SPOKE TO ME IN A FRENZIED WHISPER. THE WORDS WERE CONFUSING AT FIRST.

"I WAS IN THE EYE OF A LIVING STORM UNABLE TO HEAR MY OWN SCREAMS.

"THEN IT STOPPED, JUST LIKE THAT.

"NOTHING.

"MY PARENTS THOUGHT I HAD SOME KIND OF PANIC ATTACK... WE NEVER SPOKE ABOUT IT AGAIN.

"BUT THINGS CHANGED.

"SLOWLY AT FIRST...

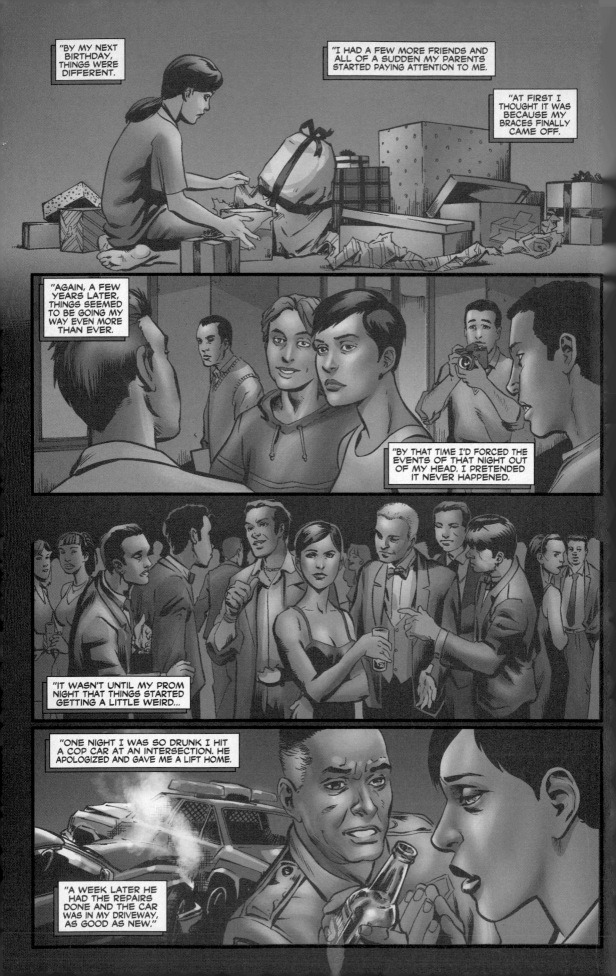

SCARSDALE

This was originally the splash page for
issue 3, which re-established where Harmony
lived. We felt since the previous issue left
off with Preston and Mickey standing on
Harmony's porch, we should pull back and
show the whole town. Jesús did a real nice job
of rendering suburbia, especially since
he lives in Spain.

DON'T STAND ALONE IN THESE STRANGEST OF TIMES

TIME TO PLAY SUPERHERO, PRESTON.

THIS IS DISGUSTING... ...THESE POOR WOMEN.

I NEVER GOT TO THANK YOU FOR NAILING THAT PSYCHO BACK AT THE TATTOO PARLOR, AGENT RINALDI.

CALL ME MICKEY AND DON'T MENTION IT. THIS IS AN UGLY SCENE.

HERE WE GO...

...AGAIN.

I KNOW I SAID IT BEFORE, BUT THIS GUY IS INSANE...

...IT'S LIKE HE'S NOT IN CONTROL OF HIMSELF.

THEY WERE ALIVE THE WHOLE TIME, SEDATED SOMEHOW...

CAN YOU GIVE ME A COMPOSITE SKETCH?

THAT'S WHY YOU'RE HERE, BRO.

LIKE PEOPLE DON'T HAVE ENOUGH TO AGONIZE ABOUT LIVING IN NEW YORK.

ROB, SOMEBODY HAS TO STOP THIS GUY.

AVENUE V.

Clyde and Robert are polar opposites, Clyde
being more of a brotherly figure to Preston
than his real brother Robert is. Everybody
knows you can't choose your family, but you
can choose your friends—and oftentimes
someone like Preston, who is alienated from
his brother, can seek out someone
that fills that role.

CLYDE

ROBERT

DISTANCE FROM ONE
INTO THE OTHER

"Love took up the harp of life, and smote on all the chords with might; Smote the chord of Self, that, trembling, passed in music out of sight."
alfred tennyson

"YOUR TIMING *SUCKS*, ROB."

"I WOULDN'T BE HERE IF IT WASN'T IMPORTANT, *PRES*."

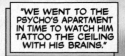

"WE WENT TO THE PSYCHO'S APARTMENT IN TIME TO WATCH HIM TATTOO THE CEILING WITH HIS BRAINS."

"SO WHAT'S THE PROBLEM? HE SAVED THE TAXPAYERS MONEY."

ROCKLAND
PSYCHIATR
HOSPITA

THAT'S WHAT I SEE, BUT IT DOESN'T MAKE SENSE.

I SHOULD HAVE EXPERIENCED *HIS* DEATH, NOT SOME RANDOM HOUSE OF HORRORS.

ROCKLAND... ROCKLAND...WHY DOES THAT SOUND *FAMILIAR?*

IT WAS A SLAUGHTERHOUSE... DOZENS...MAYBE MORE.

THIS REALLY IS THE *LAST* TIME, ROB.

CREEPY PRIEST

Much of this book—as we're sure you've noticed by now—deals with issues of trust. We expect certain people in positions of power to be worthy of our trust, but in fiction as in life there are some that abuse their power, that take advantage and use that power for their own means.

END OF NIGHT

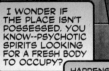

"If I had thought thou couldst have died, I might not weep for thee; but I forgot, when by thy side, that thou couldst mortal be."
charles wolfe

THERE'S ALWAYS THE CHANCE YOU COULD DIE RIGHT IN THE MIDDLE OF YOUR LIFE STORY.

MOST PEOPLE DON'T THINK OF IT.

I DO. THAT'S WHAT *SUCKS* ABOUT BEING ME.

I THINK ABOUT IT *ALL* THE TIME.

HERE I STAND, IN WHAT USED TO BE A HOSPITAL SPECIALIZING IN TREATING MENTAL ILLNESS, FOLLOWING THE GHOST TRAIL OF A SERIAL KILLER.

I WONDER IF THE PLACE ISN'T POSSESSED. YOU KNOW--PSYCHOTIC SPIRITS LOOKING FOR A FRESH BODY TO OCCUPY?

HAPPENS ON *X-FILES* ALL THE TIME.

NOT THAT I'M FANATICAL OR ANYTHING, I JUST WANT TO KNOW THAT DEATH ISN'T THE END.

FACED WITH LESS THAN A YEAR TO LIVE, IT'S SOMETHING THAT HAS BEEN ON MY MIND.

WELL, WHATEVER IT IS, ONE OF THEM HAS CONTROL OF MY BROTHER *ROBERT*...

...MAKING HIM POINT A FULLY LOADED POLICE-ISSUE HANDGUN AT MY HEAD.

NOT GOOD.

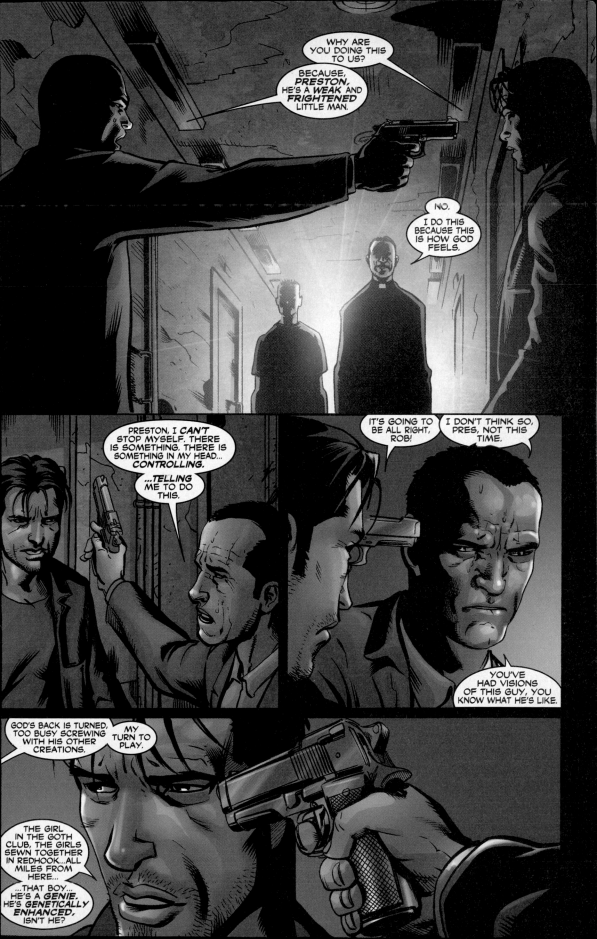

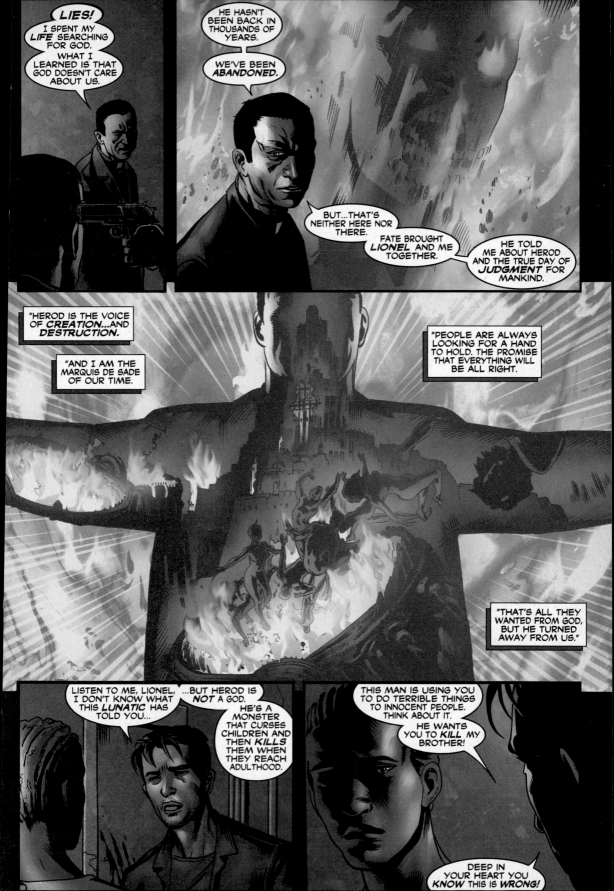

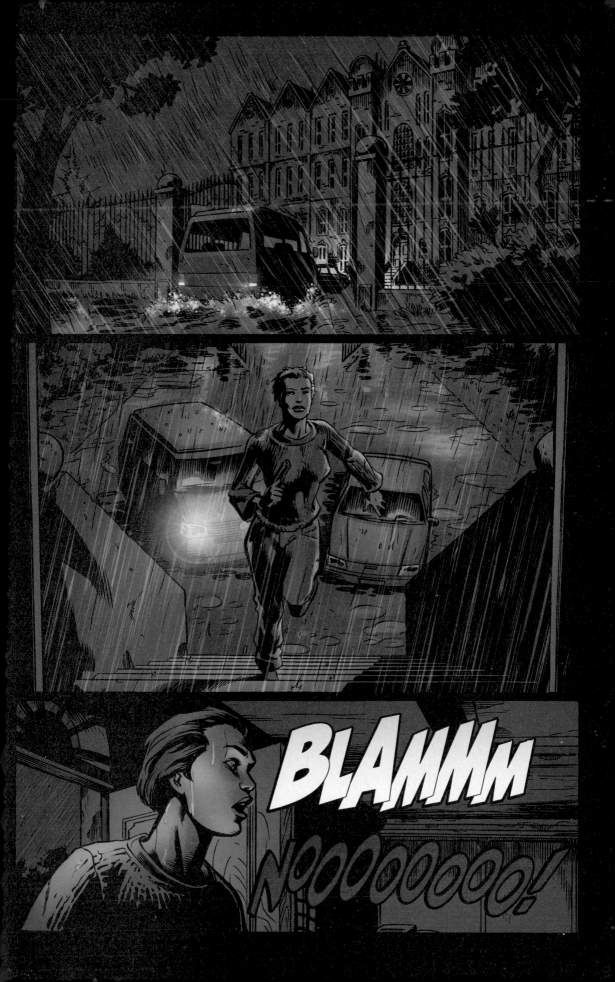

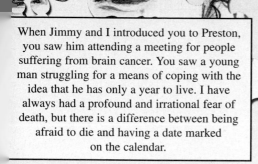

When Jimmy and I introduced you to Preston, you saw him attending a meeting for people suffering from brain cancer. You saw a young man struggling for a means of coping with the idea that he has only a year to live. I have always had a profound and irrational fear of death, but there is a difference between being afraid to die and having a date marked on the calendar.

PRESTON

Sadly and with a sense of tragic irony, in November of 2002 my aunt, whom I'd spent a number of my teen years living with, was diagnosed with a brain tumor. She was only fifty years old. It's important to her memory that you know Joan was a woman who managed to beat leukemia. She was in remission for fourteen years. She was very stubborn. She was a fighter. When the diagnosis was made the doctors gave her roughly three months to live; they gave her a date to be marked on a calendar. This news came at a time when we were working through issue 6 and the untimely death of Preston's brother Robert. The final chapter you're about to read was completed during the week following my aunt's funeral. I dedicate my contributions to 21DOWN to my aunt, Joan Hager, the stubborn fighter.

Justin Gray,
September 3rd, 2003

TRANSITIONS

*See Planetary #8.